Part Of The Rainbow

Asaf Rozanes

To my Mia
the passion, light and power behind everything I do

Mia was a normal girl,

Of a type you've often seen,

With plaits and teeth and a smiling face

And hair that was bright green

She lived at home and so did Dad,

Who also had green locks.

Dad even had green whiskers,

Green jackets and green socks.

Mia's world was happy.

Green was good and great.

She played all day with toys of green,

Until her age was eight.

That day Mia found out

The 'Old Important Rule'.

At age of eight, all the kids

Had to go to school.

Mia packed her school bag

And put her school clothes on,

She brushed her teeth and her green hair

Until they really shone.

Mia was a school girl,

Of a type you might have seen,

With school clothes and a smiling face

And hair that was bright green

At school Mia was nervous,

And shuffled in with dread,

The very first person that she met

Was a boy whose hair was red.

'How odd that is,' thought Mia,

'Red hair on a stranger,

I'm not quite sure I like it,

Red must signal danger!'

Mia walked on past the boy,

She didn't know what to do,

But just around the corner

Was a girl whose hair was blue.

Blue and red of hair on head

It made her feel quite mad.

What was wrong with green hair,

Like Mia and her dad?

Mia was a troubled girl,

She didn't know what to do,

About people who looked so different,

About hair of red and blue.

When Mia found her classroom

She nearly made a scene,

All hair colors were present

But no one else had green.

Yellow, purple, orange, gold,

Pale violet and pink,

Such a bright and brash display,

It made poor Mia blink.

Mia touched her lush, green hair

She wanted to disguise it

But she hadn't brought her cap today,

Or her woolly hat to hide it.

Mia felt so lonely,

She touched her plaited mane,

She didn't understand it,

Why wasn't everyone the same?

Mia was a confused girl,

She felt alone and sad,

She wanted now to run away

And go home to her dad.

When the teacher wandered in

He looked quite small and chummy,

His friendly eyes were sparkling,

His smile was slightly gummy.

'Sit down please class!' He uttered.

Mia heard the silence fall

'Arthur, Andrew, Bailey, Beth,'

So went the class roll call.

When the teacher called her name,

Mia felt quite shy,

She found she couldn't answer him,

Or look him in the eye.

Instead she put her hand up

And waved it in the air,

Hoping nobody would notice

Her significant green hair.

Mia was a lonely girl,

She didn't want to speak,

She didn't like her bright green hair

Didn't want to be unique.

'Ah Mia, Mia welcome!'
Said the teacher with a beam,
'Do come up and say 'hello'
And meet our colorful team.'

'We're all so glad to see you,
So glad, you couldn't know,
You're the final missing color
In our festive class rainbow!'

We need all the colors tomorrow,
For our rainbow town parade,
All the reds, golds, blues and greens,
Every single shade.

Mia was a thankful girl,

She felt a bit more serene.

It seemed quite okay after all.

To have hair that was bright green.

When Mia got home to her dad

She had so much to say.

About colors and hair and boys and girls

And tomorrow's rainbow day.

'Why have they got such strange hair?'

Asked Mia of her dad

'And when I saw it on their heads

Why did it make me sad?'

Dad laughed at his little Mia,

His princess and his queen.

'You've learned a vital lesson' He said

Not everyone is green.

'The world is bright with color,

Each pigment has its place,

Everyone is different,

Their hair, their teeth, their face.

Mia was a happy girl,

And excited about school,

She'd learned a vital lesson,

All hair color was cool!

The next day Mia skipped to school,

Dressed head to toe in green.

And all along the pavement

Dancing colors could be seen.

At school they got in order,

Mia stood in queue

Between Vincent who was yellow

And Kathy who was blue.

They danced, sang and paraded

All around the town,

Holding hands together,

Blue, green, red and brown.

Mia's world was happy now,

Her eyes were a shining glow,

She wasn't just a green girl

But part of a huge rainbow.

Mia was a wiser girl,

She now could see her place,

Different is excellent,

Unique is really ace!

Mia and Dad sprinkled and scattered love all over this book!

Were you able to notice and find all the heart shapes we scattered around?

Spoiler Alert:

The next page contains all the hidden locations, flip the page at your own risk ☺

Pssst...Here's where we hid the heart shapes:

Page 5:
On the top section of the wooden door

Page 11:
On the second school locker from the right

Page 13:
On the plant pot

Page 17:
On the plant pot

Page 19:
On the bookshelf, just above the purple books

Page 25:
On the backside of the teacher's shirt

Page 33:
On the mirror

Page 37:
On Mia's hat

If you liked our book and want to help us write many more – please take a minute and write us a review;

Reviews help us focus on what we love to do – write and draw great new books!

Join "Mia and Dad" on their journeys in these books as well:

- Short Or Tall Doesn't Matter At All
- Tomorrow Is Near But Today Is Here

and many more to come…

Want to be the first to hear about our new books and special offers?

Subscribe to our private mailing list here:

https://mindful-mia.com/subscribe

Share your thoughts and feelings about our books with us,

we'd love to hear your feedback.

Got a cool idea for a new "Mia and Dad" adventure?

Don't be shy. We read every email!

Drop us an email at:

feedback@mindful-mia.com

Thank you for joining our journey!

Love,

Mia and Dad

Mia and Dad just LOVE to color and we're sure you do too!

So we've added a few of our early book sketches just for you to color in any way you like.

Make the sky pink and the grass blue, it's all up to you!